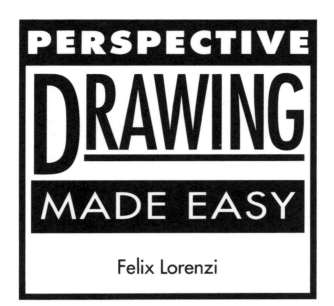

PERSPECTIVE DRAWING MADE EASY

Felix Lorenzi

D0974926

BayBooks

An imprint of HarperCollins*Publishers*

A Bay Books Publication

Bay Books, an imprint of
HarperCollins*Publishers*
25 Ryde Road, Pymble, Sydney, NSW 2073, Australia
31 View Road, Glenfield, Auckland 10, New Zealand

Published by Bay Books in 1984
This edition 1994

Copyright © Boje Verlag GmbH. Erlangen

ISBN 1 86378 178 1.

Printed in Singapore
9 8 7 6 5 4 3 2 1
97 96 95 94

Preface

In the first two volumes, you started by drawing two-dimensional pictures of animals and people. The next step was three-dimensional drawing, so you already have some idea of that. Any object in the visible world can be drawn in two dimensions or three.

In this, the third volume of the *Drawing Made Easy* series, the sketching of objects in relation to the space around them is examined: not only do objects have a third dimension but so does the space around them. Or, more correctly, every object is situated in its own particular space. For instance, a tea cup is situated in a space on top of a table; a tree stands in a large space, in a particular landscape; a person may be in a room.

The notion of space is difficult to understand, and even more difficult to draw on a two-dimensional surface (paper), so some kind of help is necessary and this is where perspective comes in. The word 'perspective' comes from Latin and means 'to look through'.

Hold a sheet of glass in front of your eyes and look through it. You will only have to go over the lines on the glass with a piece of chalk to get a three-dimensional picture. In this way, you can get three dimensions by simply copying what you see. But there are also laws of perspective, which will help you transfer three-dimensional things directly onto paper.

This is the subject of this third volume. You will find out how perspective is achieved in the following instructions.

An important concluding remark: the use of perspective is linked directly with the vantage point of the viewer. He could be standing high above a house, or in front of it, or at the bottom of a hill looking up at the house. In each case his vantage point, and therefore his horizon, will be different.

So, remember: vantage point = eye-level = horizon

In the first two volumes you have examined aspects of the visible world and tried to approach them using the same drawing method. You learnt, step by step, how people and animals can, when seen simply, be broken down into basic geometric shapes and then drawn. By starting with this simplification you are able to proceed to the complexities of free drawing.

Instructions

What is perspective?

Our world is three-dimensional. This means that we can move in it in three dimensions: left and right, up and down, and backwards and forwards.

But how can space be created on a two-dimensional surface — paper? This question involves perspective, which was quite a preoccupation for artists of earlier times. They looked for some way of giving depth to the surface they were painting, either through colour or by somehow drawing it in.

Firstly, they simply placed one object behind another so as to show which object was in the foreground and which was in the background. Later, they tried to add depth by making the objects in the background smaller. They were getting closer to a solution but it was still unsatisfactory.

The discovery that two parallel lines converge in infinity (the vanishing point) led to a new way of depicting things: by using perspective. There are two types of perspective: one-point, or parallel, perspective; and two-point, or angular, perspective. Both types are called central perspective because the radiation lines converge at the vanishing point.

Look at this picture of a completely straight railway line on a wide plain. The two rails meet at the vanishing point, like this:

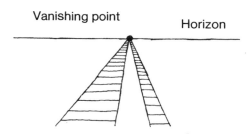

Vanishing point   Horizon

Artists soon realised that the vantage point of the viewer plays a vital role. Objects which are viewed from above (bird's eye view) look completely different from objects viewed from below (worm's eye view). Thus the term 'horizon' came into use. The horizon also refers to the eye-level, which in turn is identical to the vantage point. Look again at the example of the railway lines. Imagine your eyes are fairly close to the ground. You view the railway and the plain and this is what you see:

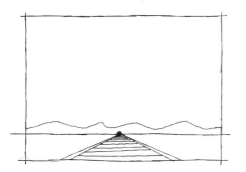

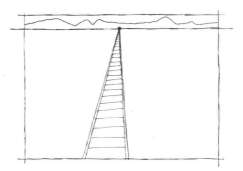

In the second example, you are standing on the ground, looking at your surroundings. The horizon, or your eye-level, has now moved to a higher position, like this:

To prove this phenomenon, take a normal sheet of glass. Place it in front of your eyes and look through it. Now, with a piece of chalk trace onto it the radiation lines you see: you will get exactly the same picture as if you had constructed it using the laws of perspective. However, your eyes must remain still to prevent any further shifting of the lines.

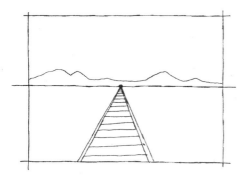

Yet another possibility arises if you stand on a high mountain. From this position, the horizon, and your eye-level, have risen even higher, like this:

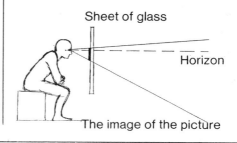

Sheet of glass

Horizon

The image of the picture

A model can be very useful here, too. It consists of a horizontal line, a vanishing point, and lines radiating from or receding into the vanishing point.

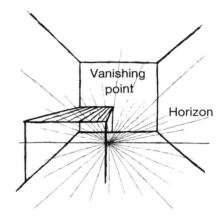

This is the first drawing in perspective. The coloured lines give the illusion of space, of a room in which a table is standing.

So, remember, all lines which in reality run parallel to each other and which appear to be receding from us (radiation lines) converge at the vanishing point. But often there is not just one vanishing point: more complex pictures sometimes contain two. Using the model it would look like this:

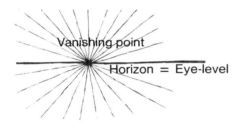

Notice that all vertical lines — walls, corners, towers, table-legs — remain vertical on your paper, just as they are in reality. Now look at the coloured lines in the following drawing.

Use this model to construct more objects. Remember that here, too, all vertical lines remain vertical.

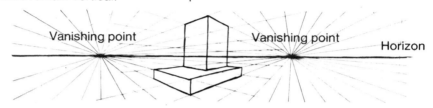

Vanishing point · Vanishing point · Horizon

Once you have grasped the principles of this model, you will be able to conjure up all sorts of different things on your paper!

This method of drawing also helps to simplify complicated objects before drawing them in detail. This is how you should always work — going from the simple to the complex.

When you have completely mastered this method, you will be able to draw correctly any object in three dimensions. This book shows you how to use the one-point and two-point perspectives.

Now, find out what happens to circles when they are drawn in perspective. Take a beautiful vase with a circular opening and a round body. When drawn in perspective, the round opening becomes an ellipse. You will see why this is so in a moment. Take a square and draw in a circle so that it fits perfectly, like this:

Diagonals determine the centre of the circle

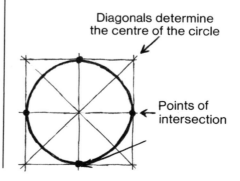

Points of intersection

There are guide lines and radiation lines. Firstly, draw the square in perspective, complete with vanishing point, of course, like this:

Vanishing point   Horizon = Eye-level

Then draw lines to connect the opposite corners — diagonals — so that the exact centre of the circle is established. Draw more radiation lines through the centre. These lines intersect with those forming the square. And, through these four points of intersection, draw in the circle which has now become an ellipse.

incorrect

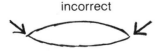

This ellipse is incorrect because the sides are pointed.

Now draw the rest of the vase.

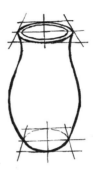

The foot of the vase is constructed in the same manner, using a second circle.

The same method can be used when drawing a tyre, like this:

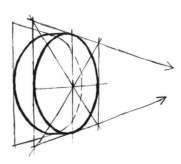

In the beginning a ruler might be useful, but later on try to avoid using one.

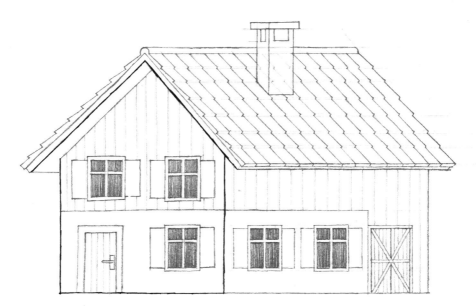

The above drawing is not in perspective. Why? Because both sides of the house have been drawn from the front. In reality this is, of course, impossible.

If you stand in front of one side of the house, the other side will appear to be receding. Its radiation lines meet at the vanishing point.

On the other hand, all the lines in the drawing below do meet at the vanishing point. The lines of the front side run parallel to the horizon. The horizon on the paper is always horizontal, and the vanishing point is found on this horizon.

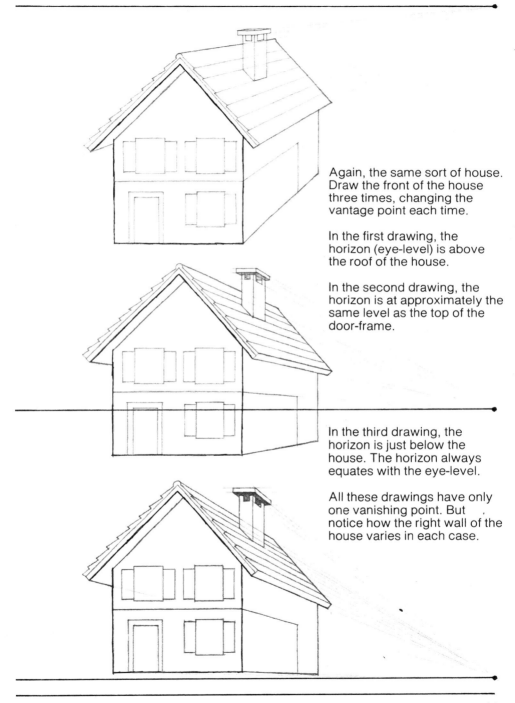

Again, the same sort of house. Draw the front of the house three times, changing the vantage point each time.

In the first drawing, the horizon (eye-level) is above the roof of the house.

In the second drawing, the horizon is at approximately the same level as the top of the door-frame.

In the third drawing, the horizon is just below the house. The horizon always equates with the eye-level.

All these drawings have only one vanishing point. But notice how the right wall of the house varies in each case.

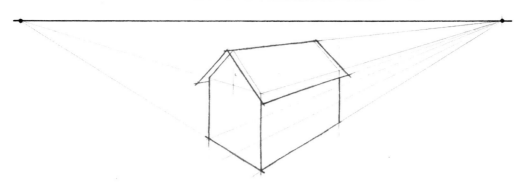

Now use two vanishing points to draw a house. It is the same house, again seen from three different levels. Notice how the front changes. In the previous drawings the lines of the front of the house ran parallel to the horizon. In these drawings, they meet at the second vanishing point.

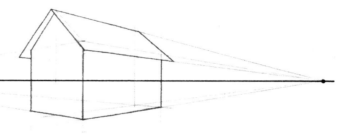

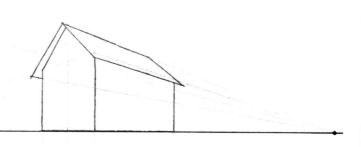

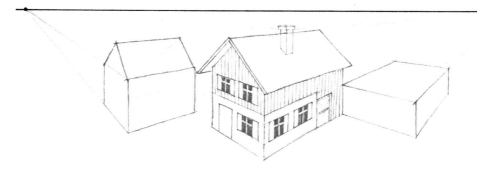

Here are some examples, showing
ways of adding other buildings.
Remember the two vanishing points.

The horizon is, of course, only an
imaginary line: it cannot actually be
seen. The same applies to the
vanishing points: they are situated in
infinity.

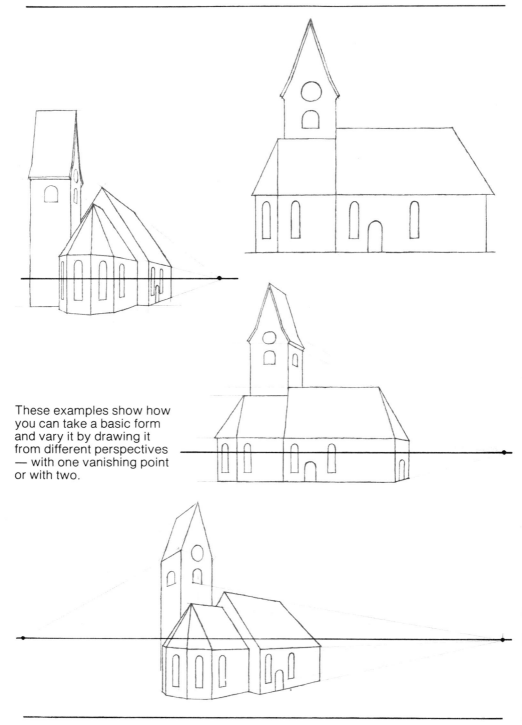

These examples show how you can take a basic form and vary it by drawing it from different perspectives — with one vanishing point or with two.

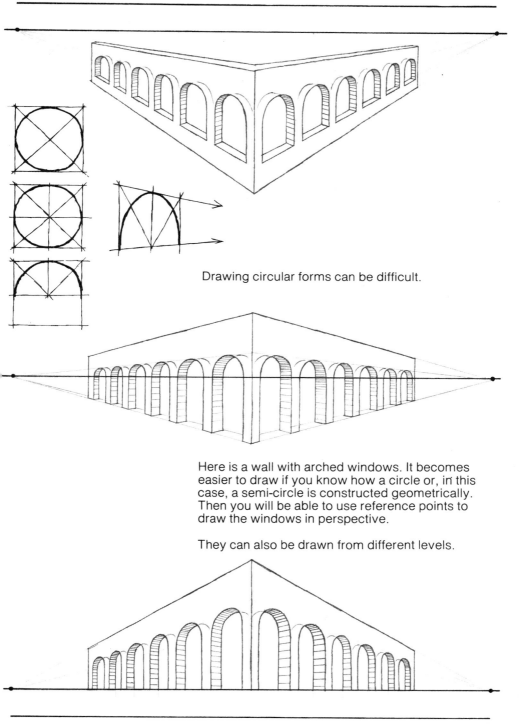

Drawing circular forms can be difficult.

Here is a wall with arched windows. It becomes easier to draw if you know how a circle or, in this case, a semi-circle is constructed geometrically. Then you will be able to use reference points to draw the windows in perspective.

They can also be drawn from different levels.

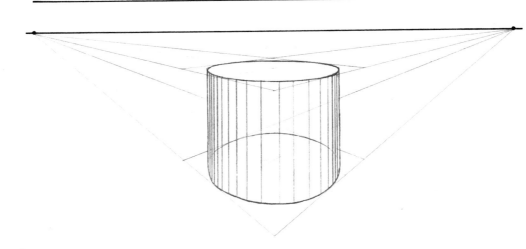

If you know how to construct circles, you will have no trouble drawing cylinders. It is best to start by first drawing a four-sided shape. Then you can draw the ellipse inside it. This method will enable you to draw things like columns and tyres.

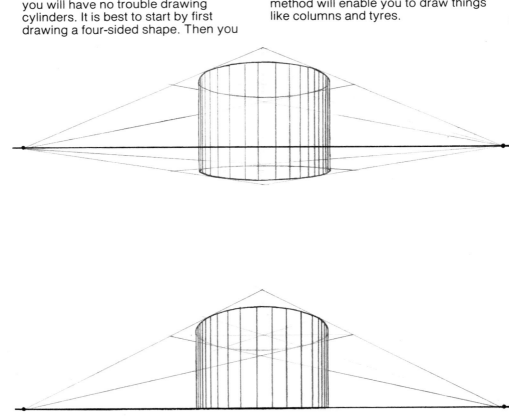

This drawing uses everything you have learnt so far. Try to complete it. The two vanishing points are there. Think up some new constructions!

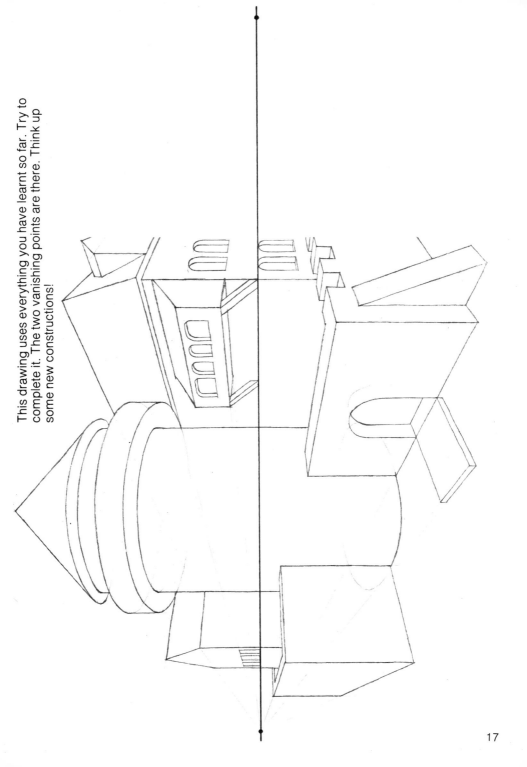

All sorts of surprises are found in the
kitchen cupboards!

It's just a matter of finding them.
Practise what you have learnt by
drawing simple objects.

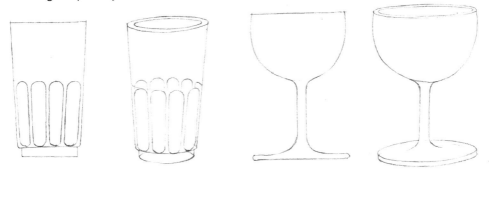

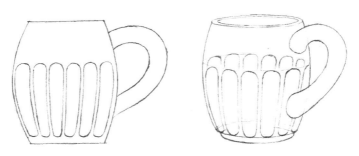

In the living room there is any number
of things that you can try to draw by
using perspective.

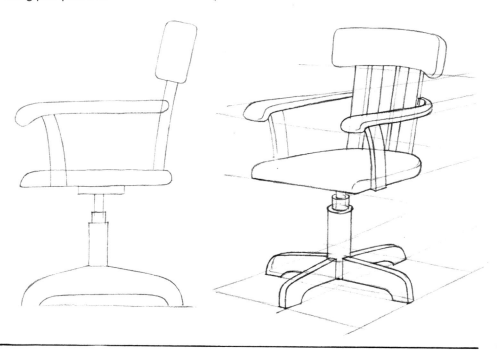

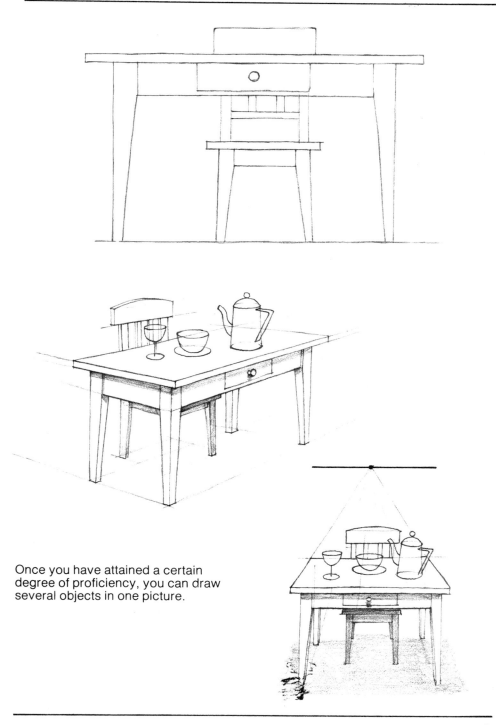

Once you have attained a certain degree of proficiency, you can draw several objects in one picture.

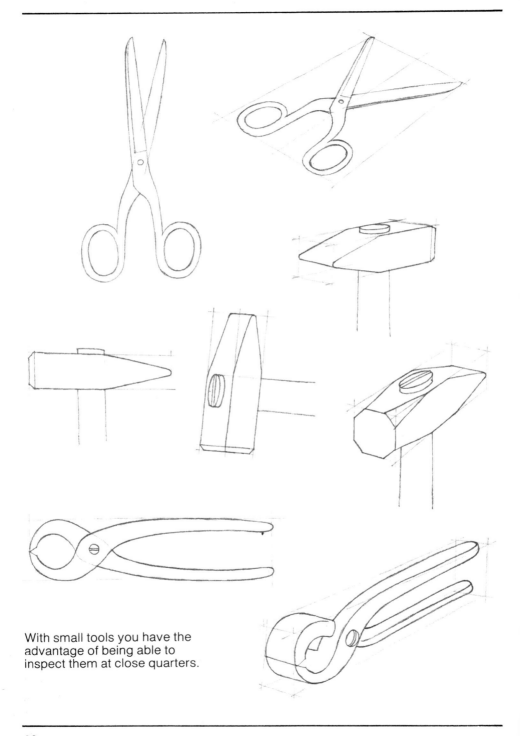

With small tools you have the advantage of being able to inspect them at close quarters.

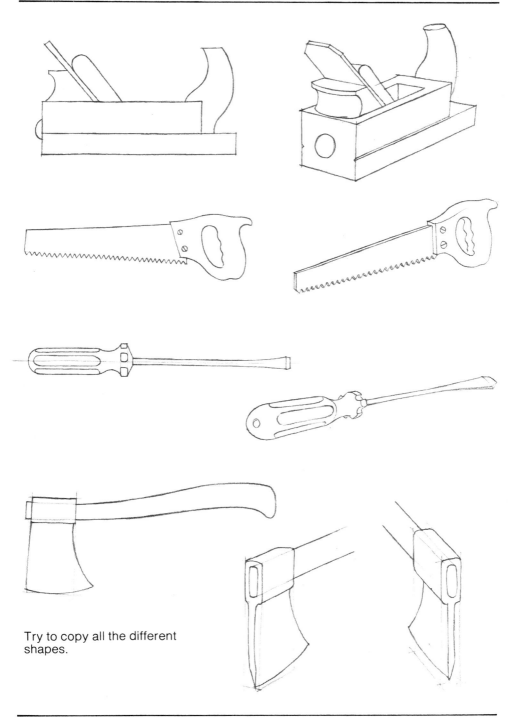

Try to copy all the different shapes.

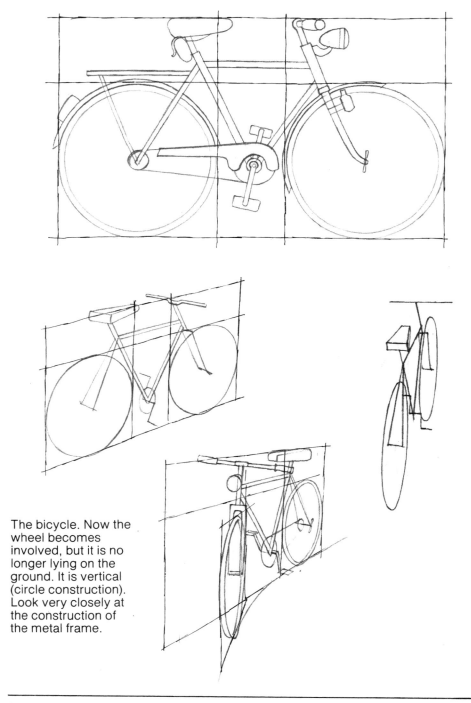

The bicycle. Now the wheel becomes involved, but it is no longer lying on the ground. It is vertical (circle construction). Look very closely at the construction of the metal frame.

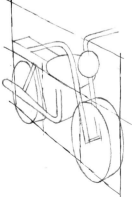

A motor-bike. Try to work out
just how a motor-bike is built.
Examine it thoroughly.

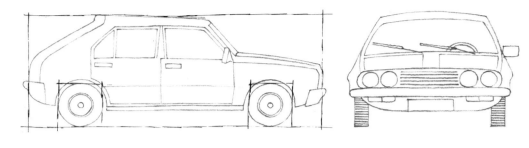

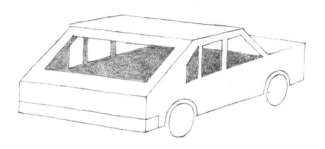

The ubiquitous car. Firstly, try to draw a 'box-car'. Once you have drawn this basic form, you can adapt it and thus gradually come closer to the actual shape of the car. It helps to add some shading so that you can see the difference between the inside and the outside of the car more clearly. In this way the picture becomes more life-like.

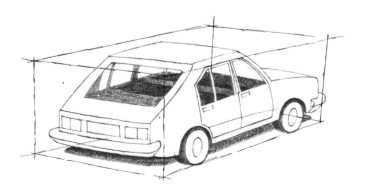

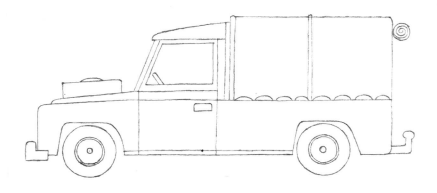

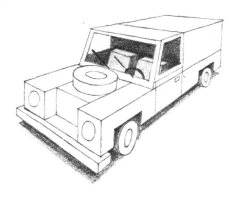

A four-wheel drive for a long trip. Try
thinking up some stories to illustrate!

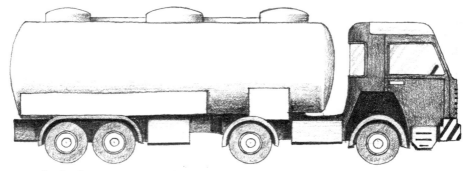

And, of course, remember trucks. In this first drawing, the artist is standing right in front of one of these giants.

Now he is looking down at the truck from the first floor of a building.

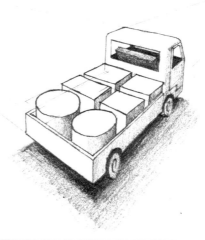

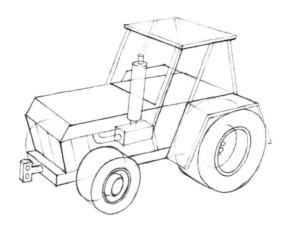

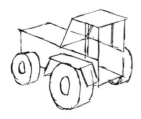

What does a tractor really look like?
Here are two different drawings.

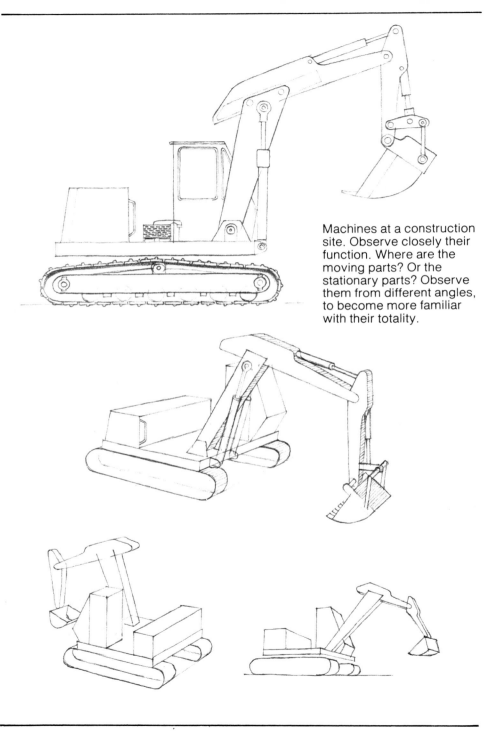

Machines at a construction site. Observe closely their function. Where are the moving parts? Or the stationary parts? Observe them from different angles, to become more familiar with their totality.

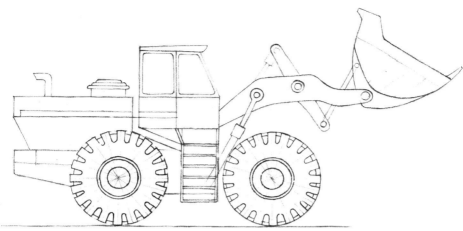

A heavy bulldozer. Which of its parts is involved when the scoop is raised or lowered?

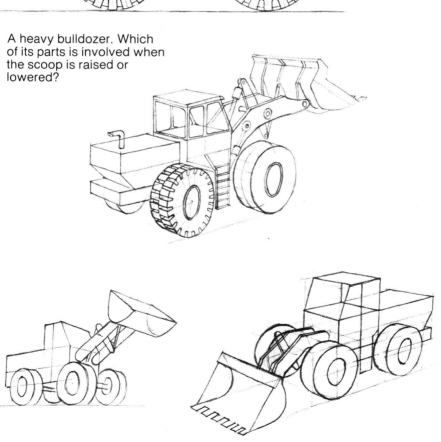

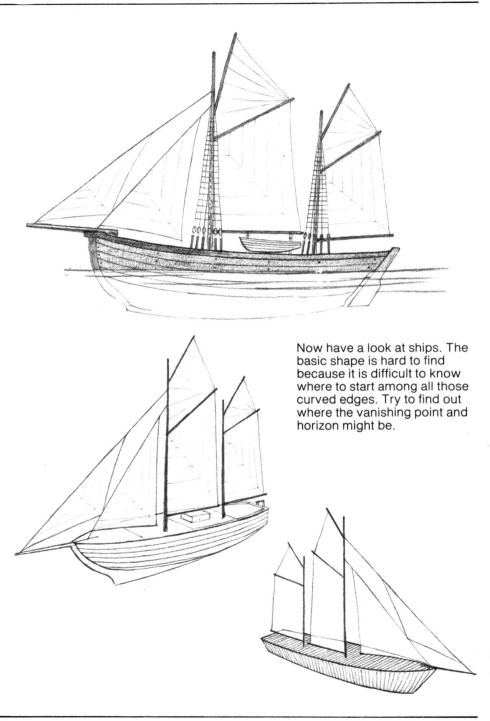

Now have a look at ships. The basic shape is hard to find because it is difficult to know where to start among all those curved edges. Try to find out where the vanishing point and horizon might be.

With close observation, and a bit of practice, you will easily solve this problem.

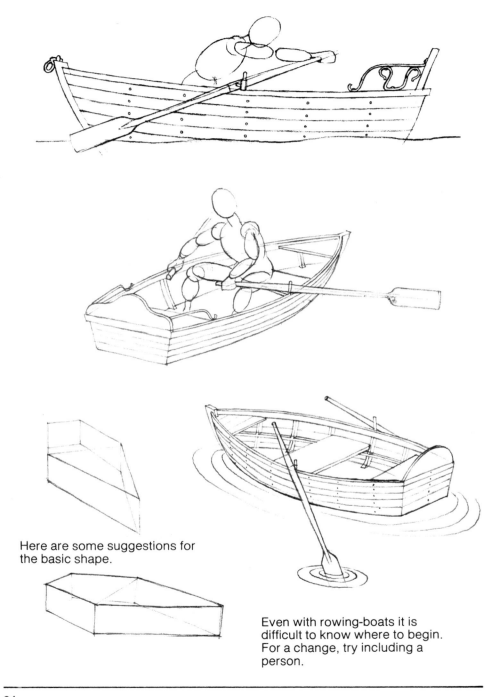

Here are some suggestions for the basic shape.

Even with rowing-boats it is difficult to know where to begin. For a change, try including a person.

The canoe was an important means of
transport for the heroes of adventure
stories. Try to find a basic shape here,
too.

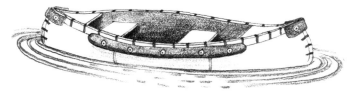

Here are some examples.

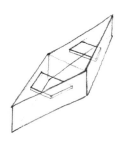

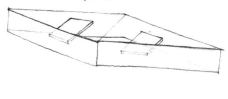

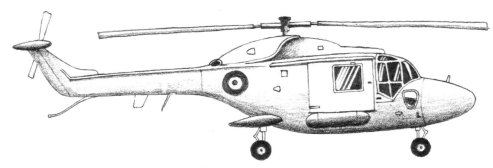

The helicopter. A complicated shape and another one where it is difficult to find a starting point because all the shapes are rounded. Look for a suitable basic shape.

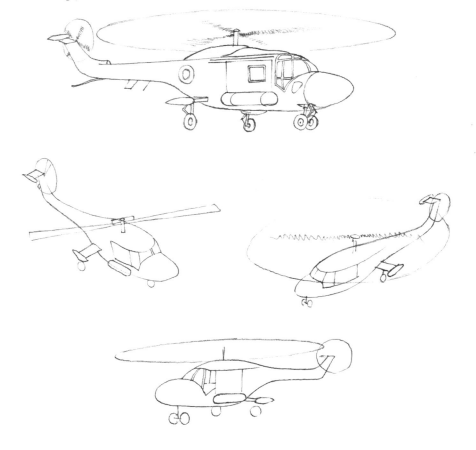

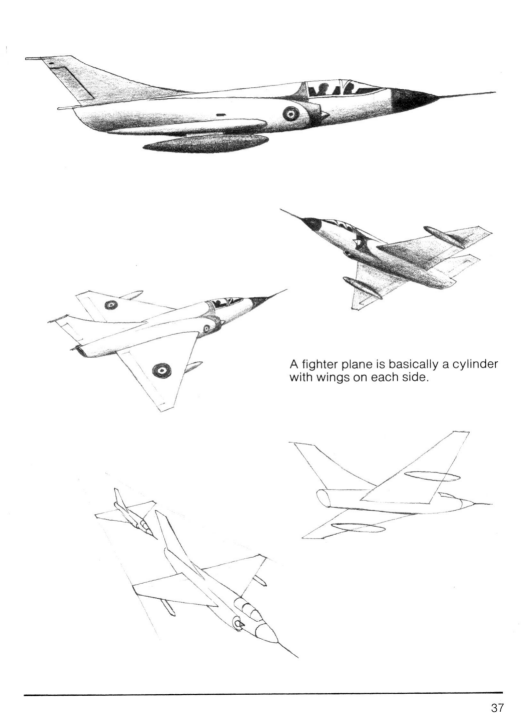

A fighter plane is basically a cylinder with wings on each side.

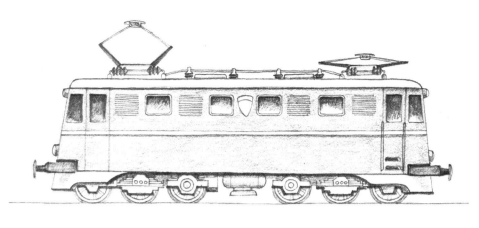

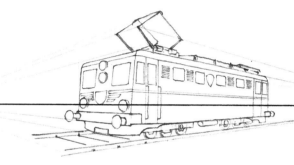

Try to sketch the various shapes of
new and old locomotives.

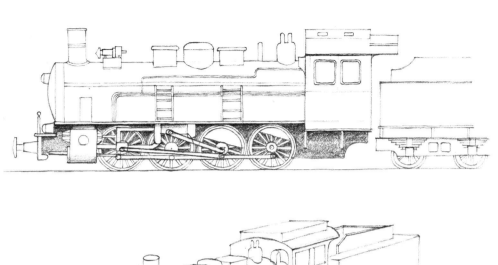

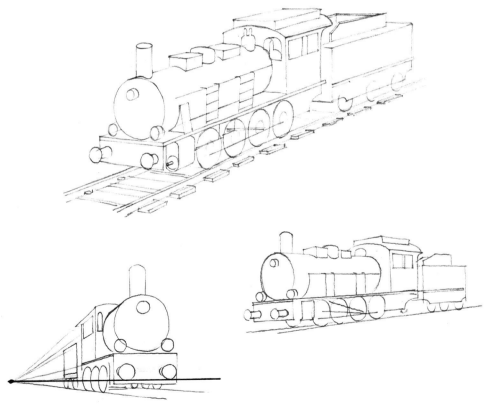

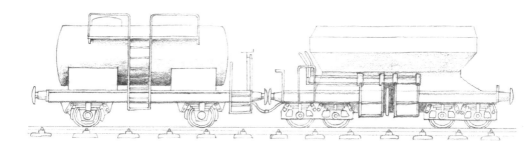

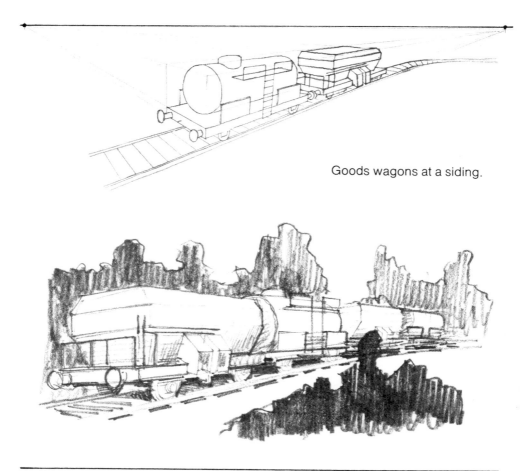

Goods wagons at a siding.

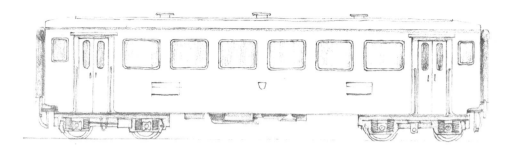

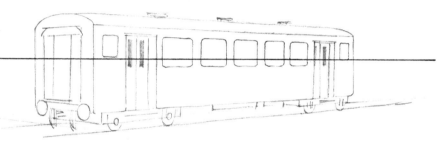

A passenger train. Draw it and then add some scenery. Closer trees will be large, and those further away will appear smaller.

Here are some examples. The guide lines have more or less disappeared, and there is no vanishing point.

If the artist is a clever observer he has no need of these aids; he can see immediately the angle of each line in terms of the horizon.

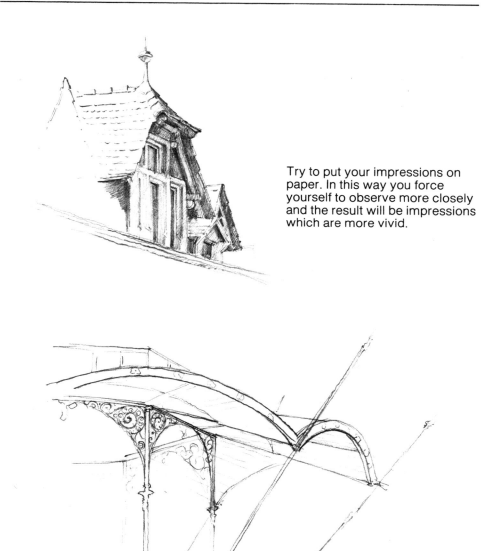

Try to put your impressions on paper. In this way you force yourself to observe more closely and the result will be impressions which are more vivid.

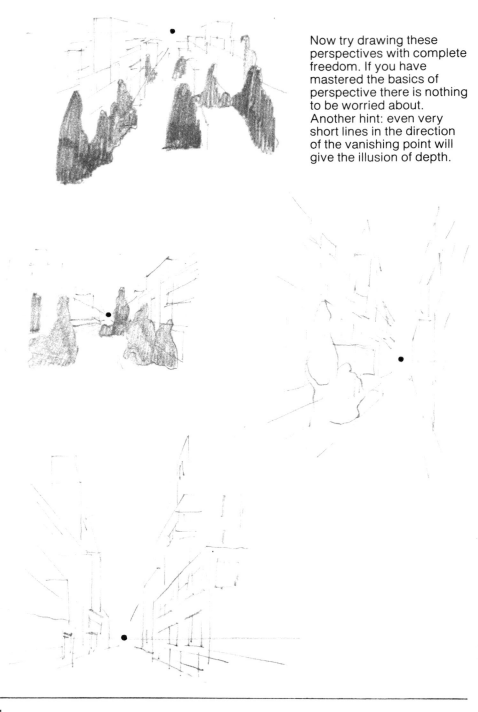

Now try drawing these perspectives with complete freedom. If you have mastered the basics of perspective there is nothing to be worried about. Another hint: even very short lines in the direction of the vanishing point will give the illusion of depth.

Now add some trees.

And, finally, another way of doing three-dimensional drawings: shading. The upper end of the grey scale consists of a number of different shades of grey. If you look closely you will see that they give an illusion of depth. The two-dimensional surface appears to bend forward. This phenomenon can also be used in simple drawings. Look at the examples below. In the first one, the same shade of grey is used throughout and there is no illusion of depth. But, in the second one, the edges are a little darker, with the result that the picture appears to be curved. So, you see, perspective lines are not the only means of creating an impression of depth.

Here is an example of the use of both methods, radiation lines and shades of grey.

This is a three-dimensional example using simple geometric shapes. Different shades of grey create an illusion of depth.

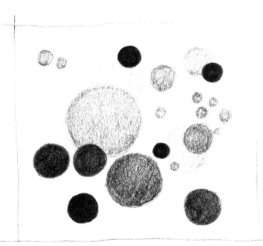

See the difference between a circle and a sphere? The sphere can really only be drawn properly if it is shaded.

Conclusion

The comments made at the beginning of the series also apply to this volume: to be able to draw you must first learn to observe. Drawing what you see will make you become much more aware of your surroundings. If you have never tried to use perspective when drawing you may have had difficulty appreciating architecture, both past and present, and understanding the secrets of spatial relationships. Like the other volumes in the series, this book is by no means meant only for the talented artist. Rather, it is designed to help anyone who thinks he might enjoy drawing. And surely you can see that learning to draw is worth the effort!